# CATCH A SHARK

## AND OTHER PREHISTORIC SEA MONSTERS

Susan Hayes

Consultant: Dr Neil DL Clark
Hunterian Museum, University of Glasgow

# CONTENTS

# There are SHARKS

and other prehistoric sea monsters

## in this book!

SOMEONE left the door OPEN. The door to another dimension, where time is all MIXED UP. And before anyone noticed, a medley of PREHISTORIC SEA CREATURES got through!

Mosasaurs, pliosaurs, plesiosaurs, ichthyosaurs, and ancient sharks, whales, and fish appeared. They prowled the ocean depths, terrorized the seas, and patrolled the rivers and the swamps. *Liopleurodon*, MEGALODON, *Archelon*, SUCHOMIMUS, *Tylosaurus*, DUNKLEOSTEUS, *Shonisaurus*, LIVYATAN, and many MORE entered OUR WORLD.

BUT then a strange thing happened. The creatures dissolved into thin air, and were nowhere to be seen. It wasn't until darkness fell that they became apparent.

Darkness is NO CLOAK for these mighty, ferocious, and EXTRAORDINARY beasts. In the dark, they can hide no longer. Instead, they shine and glow like beacons of the night.

# You must CATCH them!

At the moment the ancient sharks and sea monsters are hiding in different places in THIS book. It is your job to find them, keep an eye on them, and make sure they do not escape again. ALL YOU HAVE TO DO IS—

1. Study the CREATURE
2. Look at the CLUES
3. Find the HABITAT
4. Turn out the LIGHTS

When you find each sea monster, if they glow brightly, we are all safe. DO NOT let them ESCAPE! They are DANGEROUS in the outside WORLD—to themselves, and to you.

## PLEASE!!

DO NOT tip the book upside down. DO NOT shake it. DO NOT leave the room with the book OPEN. And DO NOT use it to swat flies.

# How do you CATCH a SEA MONSTER?

It's simple. Just study the CLUES, find the HABITAT, and turn out the LIGHTS.

To make sure you've found all the prehistoric sharks, river and sea monsters, check page 48.

## How to catch LIOPLEURODON

## 1. Study the CLUES

Each creature has its own CLUES box. Study it carefully.

*Liopleurodon* hunts large marine creatures such as DOLPHINS and ICHTHYOSAURS. Which habitat do you think it is hiding in?

coral reef
kelp forest
open sea
river
school of fish
shipwreck
jellyfish bloom
swamp

**These CLUES will help you to find where *LIOPLEURODON* is hiding in this book:**

 Eyes on the top of head to catch prey from below. **Look for prey such as dolphins.**

 Preys on ichthyosaurs. **Have you found *Eurhinosaurus* yet?**

 Must surface to breathe. Check the ocean surface.

 Now turn to the GLOW-IN-THE-DARK habitat pages to catch *LIOPLEURODON*!

There is MORE information on the Liopleurodon page that can help you, too:

**HUGE JAWS** take up one-fifth of *Liopleurodon's* body length.

6

# 2. Find the HABITAT

Did you find a dolphin in the OPEN SEA?

*Liopleurodon* ambushes prey at high speed. It can accelerate quickly to catch dolphins and other marine animals.

## REMEMBER!
All animals must EAT. They will look for a habitat that provides them with FOOD.

# 3. Turn off the LIGHTS

What else is HIDING in this habitat?

The ichthyosaur *Eurhinosaurus* is leaping out of the water to esacpe *Liopleurodon's* mighty jaws.

When you turn out the lights, *LIOPLEURODON* will appear.

It will GLOW in the DARK.

Are you READY to CATCH the other prehistoric CREATURES?

# MEGALODON
is the terror of the OCEAN. It is the BIGGEST shark EVER!

 GOOD EYESIGHT, even in murky and dark waters.

 MEGA TEETH, up to 7 inches long. They are razor-sharp and serrated like steak knives.

**MEGALODON** has the most powerful bite of any creature that's ever lived. It is four to six times more powerful than the bite of a T-rex, and almost 30 times stronger than the bite of a modern lion. This giant shark could crush a small car easily.

 GIANT JAW, which can open wide enough to swallow a hippopotamus whole.

 WORN AND BROKEN TEETH are replaced quickly. *Megalodon* goes through thousands of teeth in a lifetime.

## ID KIT

*MEGALODON* (MEGA-ah-low-don)

**MEANING** big tooth

**FOSSILS FOUND** worldwide

**WHEN** Late Oligocene

**LENGTH** up to 60 feet

**WEIGHT** up to 110 tons

**DIET** carnivore

**FOOD** sharks, whales, dolphins, turtles, dugongs, manatees, seals

These CLUES will help you to find where *MEGALODON* is hiding in this book:

 Giant jaw to eat large marine creatures. **Look for prey.**

 Megalodon is HUGE! **You won't miss it.**

 Hunts the same prey as *Livyatan*. **Find this prehistoric whale.**

 Now turn to the GLOW-IN-THE-DARK habitat pages to catch *MEGALODON*!

DORSAL FIN to stabilize against rolling and to assist in sudden turns.

**A BABY MEGALODON** is as big as the biggest modern great white. A Megalodon pup is able to hunt soon after birth, so it can take care of itself straight away.

10-FOOT TAIL FIN to push forward in the water. *Megalodon* can reach speeds of 20 miles per hour to outrun prey.

AIRPLANE-LIKE FINS to help support the weight of its enormous jaws and head.

**DOLPHINS, SHARKS, AND SEALS** are easy prey for this mega shark. It attacks shoulders, spines, and ribs in order to crush vital body organs inside. When Megalodon hunts larger prey, such as whales, it bites fins first so they can't swim away.

# DEINOSUCHUS likes dinosaur for DINNER. It is a SUPERCROC.

**AMBUSH!** *DEINOSUCHUS* grabs prey with its jaws and drags it into the water. Then it turns over and over to drown its catch.

**HUGE BODY.** *Deinosuchus* doesn't ever stop growing. It might live for more than 50 years, so can get VERY big!

 **POWERFUL BITE** to hunt large and armored animals.

 **HUGE JAWS** contain over 90 teeth. The sharp front teeth tear flesh. The blunt back ones crush bone.

## ID KIT

**DEINOSUCHUS** (DY-no-SU-kus)

**MEANING** terrible crocodile

**FOSSILS FOUND** USA, Mexico

**WHEN** Cretaceous

**LENGTH** up to 35 feet

**WEIGHT** up to 8 tons

**DIET** carnivore

**FOOD** fish, turtles, dinosaurs

These **CLUES** will help you to find where *DEINOSUCHUS* is hiding in this book:

 Lives in fresh water. **Look for a river or a swamp.**

 Powerful bite to hunt dinosaurs and turtles. **Find its prey.**

 Ambushes prey. **Look on the riverbed.**

Now turn to the GLOW-IN-THE-DARK habitat pages to catch *DEINOSUCHUS*!

**LARGE TURTLES** make a tasty meal. *Deinosuchus* waits on the river bed. It can crunch right through a turtle's shell.

# TYLOSAURUS is a giant mosasaur. It EATS almost ANYTHING.

**TYLOSAURUS** must surface to breathe. If a pterosaur or a bird is in its way, it will be dinner.

LONG SNOUT is used for fighting to gain control of an area with plenty of food.

LARGE TEETH and strong jaws to eat large prey, including other mosasaurs.

THIS *PTERANODON* is likely to disappear into *Tylosaurus's* powerful jaws.

REINFORCED SNOUT for ramming prey. Marine reptiles are killed outright or stunned into floating helplessly on the surface.

Mosasaurs have long snake-like bodies. *Tylosaurus* uses its tail to propel it through warm, shallow seas. It isn't very fast, so surprises prey by attacking from below.

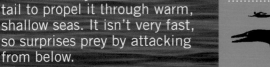

## ID KIT

**TYLOSAURUS** (TIE-lo-SORE-us)

**MEANING** knob lizard

**FOSSILS FOUND** Canada, USA

**WHEN** Late Cretaceous

**LENGTH** up to 46 feet

**WEIGHT** 20 tons

**DIET** carnivore

**FOOD** sharks, large fish, turtles, ammonites, smaller mosasaurs, large marine reptiles, pterosaurs

These **CLUES** will help you to find where *TYLOSAURUS* is hiding in this book:

 Large teeth to eat sharks, turtles, and smaller mosasaurs. **Find its prey.**

 Enormous snout for territorial combat. **Watch out for this feature.**

 Swims in warm, shallow seas. **Look for sunlit waters.**

Now turn to the GLOW-IN-THE-DARK habitat pages to catch *TYLOSAURUS*!

# SHONISAURUS looks like a TUBBY DOLPHIN! It is a gigantic ichthyosaur.

LARGE EYES to hunt in deep, dark waters.

LONG, TOOTHLESS SNOUT. Young are born with teeth for self-defense, but the teeth fall out as they get older.

## ID KIT

**SHONISAURUS**

(SHOW-nee-SORE-us)

**COMMON NAME** Shoshone lizard

**FOSSILS FOUND** USA

**WHEN** Late Triassic

**LENGTH** up to 50 feet

**WEIGHT** up to 35 tons

**DIET** carnivore

**FOOD** squid, soft fish

These CLUES will help you to find where *SHONISAURUS* is hiding in this book:

 Toothless jaw for eating soft fish and squid. **Look for prey.**

 A huge ichthyosaur. **Find a big creature.**

 No defense except for size. It won't share a habitat with larger predators.

 Now turn to the GLOW-IN-THE-DARK habitat pages to catch *SHONISAURUS*!

HUGE, ROUND BODY. *Shonisaurus* is so big that it is not threatened by most predators.

DORSAL FIN
for stability.

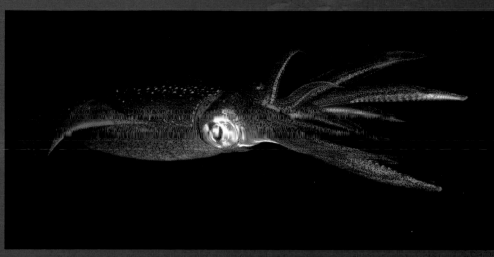

**SHONISAURUS** doesn't have teeth, so soft fish and squid are a perfect meal. Its large eyes mean that it can see to hunt in the dark.

THICK FISH-LIKE TAIL. *Shonisaurus* is a relatively slow swimmer.

**ICHTHYOSAURS** surface to breathe air. They don't have gills, so can't breathe underwater. It is likely that it can hold its breath for over an hour like a modern sperm whale.

LONG FLIPPERS
for moving through the ocean.

**LIKE MODERN DOLPHINS,** *Shonisaurus* lives in large pods, or groups. It gives birth to live young, which learn about hunting and survival from the pod.

**ARCHELON** travels long distances in the **OPEN OCEAN**. It is the biggest turtle **EVER**.

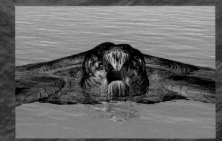

*ARCHELON* swims to a sandy beach to mate and to lay eggs. It buries its eggs in a hole, in the dark of night.

**HEAD AND FLIPPERS** cannot be pulled inside its shell. It is an easy target for sharks and mosasaurs.

**BARNACLES AND PARASITES** attach themselves to *Archelon's* vast bony shell.

**POWERFUL HOOKED BEAK** to break open shelled animals such as ammonites.

**HUGE FLIPPERS** for long distance travel in the sunlit zone near to the ocean surface.

## ID KIT

*ARCHELON* (ARK-eh-lon)

**MEANING** large turtle

**FOSSILS FOUND** USA

**WHEN** Late Cretaceous

**LENGTH** 15 feet

**WEIGHT** 2 tons

**DIET** omnivore

**FOOD** jellyfish, ammonites, belemnites, seaweed, squid

These **CLUES** will help you to find where *ARCHELON* is hiding in this book:

 Swims near to the ocean surface. **Find a sunlit ocean.**

 Hooked beak to cut up prey. **Search for jellyfish.**

 Unprotected flippers make *Archelon* an easy target for large predators. **Look for sharks and mosasaurs.**

 Now turn to the GLOW-IN-THE-DARK habitat pages to catch ARCHELON!

*JELLYFISH* are an important part of *Archelon's* diet. Its sharp horned beak snips the jellyfish into bite-sized pieces.

# DAKOSAURUS

is a large, fierce **CROCODILE** that spends its life **AT SEA**.

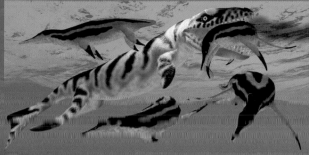

**LARGE MARINE ANIMALS** such as ichthyosaurs and plesiosaurs are on *Dakosaurus's* dinner menu. It often twist feeds, which means that it tears chunks of flesh from its living prey.

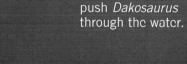

FISH-LIKE TAIL to push *Dakosaurus* through the water.

TALL, DEEP SKULL with a powerful jaw for eating large marine reptiles.

POWERFUL FLIPPERS for swimming and for steering.

SAW-LIKE TEETH to slice flesh into small and digestible chunks.

## ID KIT

*DAKOSAURUS* (DACK-oh-SORE-us)

**MEANING** tearing lizard

**FOSSILS FOUND** North America, South America, Europe, Russia

**WHEN** Late Jurassic to Early Cretaceous

**LENGTH** up to 16 feet

**WEIGHT** up to 1 ton

**DIET** carnivore

**FOOD** fish, squid, marine reptiles

These **CLUES** will help you to find where *DAKOSAURUS* is hiding in this book:

Adapted to live in salty sea water. **Find an ocean.**

Eats large fish. **Spot** *Dakosaurus's* **prey.**

Four powerful flippers. **Look out for this feature.**

Now turn to the GLOW-IN-THE-DARK habitat pages to catch *DAKOSAURUS!*

*DAKOSAURUS* snares large fish with its serrated, or saw-like, teeth. But it also eats much larger marine animals.

# KRONOSAURUS is named after Kronus, a POWERFUL and SAVAGE titan from Ancient Greek legend.

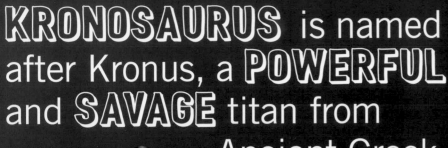

**KRONOSAURUS** could easily crush large ammonites in the Early Cretaceous oceans. Its fang-like teeth are the size of small bananas!

**LONG, SMOOTH, CONICAL TEETH** to spear prey and swallow them whole.

**HUGE 9-FOOT HEAD** is one and a half times the size of a man.

**POWERFUL JAWS** to clamp onto large prey and tear off chunks of flesh.

## ID KIT

**KRONOSAURUS**

(KROW-no-SORE-us)

**MEANING** Kronus lizard

**FOSSILS FOUND** Australia, Colombia

**WHEN** Early Cretaceous

**LENGTH** up to 32 feet

**WEIGHT** 10 tons

**DIET** carnivore

**FOOD** plesiosaurs, pliosaurs, squid, ammonites, turtles, fish

These CLUES will help you to find where **KRONOSAURUS** is hiding in this book:

Swallows small prey whole. **Find some fish.**

Huge banana-sized teeth! **Spot this feature.**

Powerful jaws to clamp onto large marine reptiles. **Look for plesiosaurs.**

Now turn to the GLOW-IN-THE-DARK habitat pages to catch **KRONOSAURUS**!

KRONOSAURUS **IS CAMOUFLAGED** in the ocean. When viewed from below, its lighter belly blends in with the lighter sky above. When viewed from above, its darker back blends in with the ocean bottom underneath. This is called countershading.

SHORT TAPERED TAIL may help with steering.

THICK MUSCULAR BODY moves quickly through the ocean.

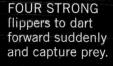

FOUR STRONG flippers to dart forward suddenly and capture prey.

KRONOSAURUS **LUNGES** forward to catch its prey. This includes a 20-foot-long Rhizodus fish, which is longer than a modern great white shark.

17

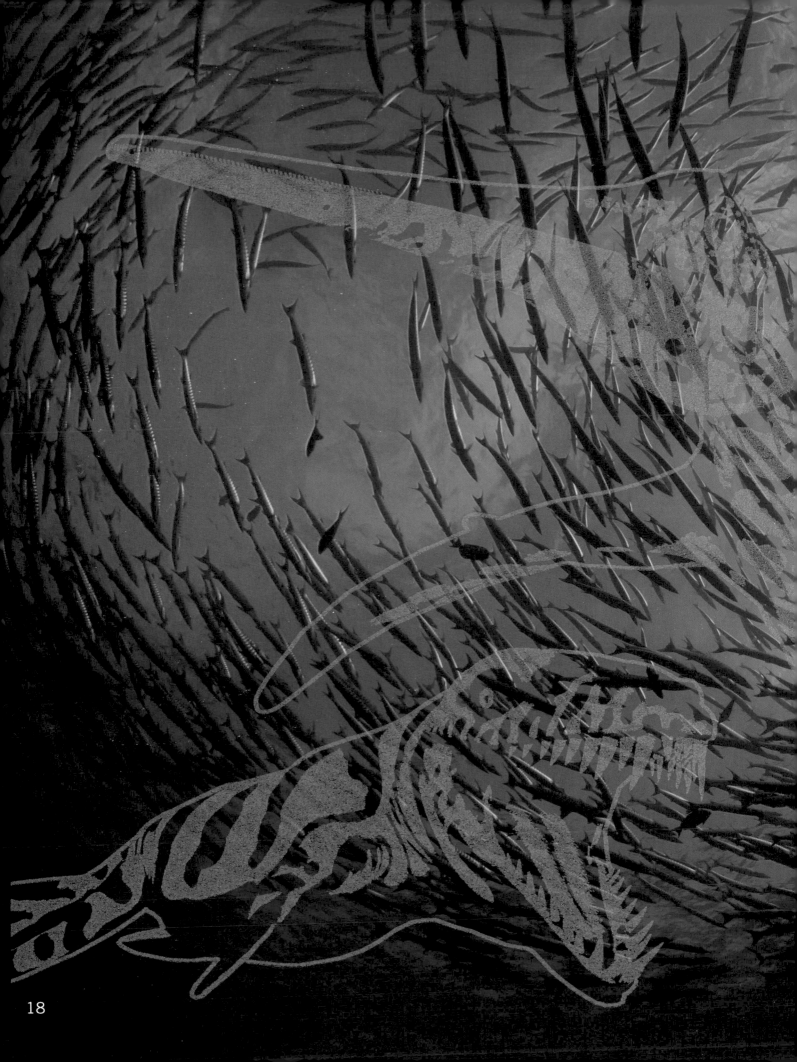

## SCHOOL OF FISH CLUES

plankton     sunlit ocean     fish     squid

# LIVYATAN attacks its victims from **BELOW**. It grips onto prey with its huge **TEETH**.

**SHORT WIDE SNOUT** for ramming into prey and headbutting other males in mating contests. It may also be used for echolocation.

**STRONG JAW-CLOSING MUSCLES** to bite down powerfully with its huge front teeth.

**GIANT INTERLOCKING TEETH** for piercing flesh. These 14-inch daggers are the largest biting teeth of any known animal.

## ID KIT

*LIVYATAN* (LIV-ya-TAN)

**MEANING** twisted in folds

**FOSSILS FOUND** Peru

**WHEN** Late Miocene

**LENGTH** up to 60 feet

**WEIGHT** at least 50 tons

**DIET** carnivore

**FOOD** baleen whales, sharks, seals, dolphins

These **CLUES** will help you to find where *LIVYATAN* is hiding in this book:

 Strong jaw to bite large marine animals. **Look for dolphins.**

 Hunts for the same prey as *Megalodon.* **Have you spotted this prehistoric shark yet?**

 It is 50 feet long. **You won't miss it!**

 Now turn to the GLOW-IN-THE-DARK habitat pages to catch a *LIVYATAN*!

**MONSTER SHARK MEGALODON** hunted in the same oceans as *Livyatan* 9-10 million years ago. A meeting would have been ferocious and messy.

# STYXOSAURUS uses its very long neck to AMBUSH PREY.

SMALL STONES, or gastroliths, in stomach to rub off fish scales and grind up bones. The stones help with digestion.

LONG NECK, at least half the length of its body, to reach into shoals of fish.

**STYXOSAURUS ARE SLOW SWIMMERS**. They are vulnerable to large predatory sharks and mosasaurs.

SHARP, CONICAL TEETH for holding onto prey, before swallowing it whole.

**BELEMNITES** were plentiful in the Late Cretaceous period. *Styxosaurus* feasted on these squid-like creatures, as well as on fish and ammonites.

## ID KIT

*STYXOSAURUS*

(STICKS-oh-SORE-rus)

**MEANING** Styx lizard

**FOSSILS FOUND** USA

**WHEN** Late Cretaceous

**LENGTH** 38 feet

**WEIGHT** 6 tons

**DIET** piscivore

**FOOD** fish, ammonites, belemnites

**These CLUES will help you to find where *STYXOSAURUS* is hiding in this book:**

Long neck for reaching into shoals of fish. **Look for fish.**

Swallows gastroliths to help with digestion. **Find small stones.**

Eats ammonites. **Did these prehistoric creatures find their way into your book?**

Now turn to the **GLOW-IN-THE-DARK** habitat pages to catch *STYXOSAURUS*!

# SWAMP CLUES

fresh water · fish · turtles · riverbed

CATCH ME if you can!

# XENACANTHUS is an eel-like SHARK. It HUNTS in fresh water river systems.

*XENACANTHUS* crunches small creatures from the river bed with its unusual teeth. If there isn't enough food, it eats its own young.

RIBBON-LIKE FIN runs the entire length of *Xenacanthus's* body and around its tail.

MOVEABLE SPINE for defense. It is long, sharp, and may be poisonous.

SLIM, EEL-LIKE BODY moves swiftly through the water.

## ID KIT

*XENACANTHUS*

(ZEE-nah-CAN-thus)

**MEANING** foreign spike

**FOSSILS FOUND** USA, Europe, India

**WHEN** Devonian to Triassic

**LENGTH** 3 feet

**DIET** carnivore

**FOOD** crustaceans, bony fish

These CLUES will help you to find where XENACANTHUS is hiding in this book:

 This shark does not live in the sea. Find fresh water.

 It eats fish. **Look for freshwater fish.**

 *Xenacanthus* has a slim eel-like body. **Look for this feature.**

 Now turn to the GLOW-IN-THE-DARK habitat pages to catch XENACANTHUS!

 UNUSUAL V-SHAPED TEETH, each with two sharp points.

**THREE HUNDRED MILLION** years ago, *Xenacanthus* was hunted by *Eryops*. This large and stocky amphibian ate its prey whole.

# TRILOBITES can be smooth or spiky, SMALL or LARGE.

**THERE ARE MORE** than 20,000 different types of trilobite, which swim, crawl, or drift through the ocean. They can be predators, scavengers, or filter feeders.

*ANOMALOCARIS* hunted trilobites 450 million years ago. This 2-3 foot predator sucked its victim's soft body from its shell.

SEGMENTS allow some trilobites to curl up for protection, just like a modern pillbug.

CEPHALON, or head, hides the trilobite's mouth.

LARGE CURVED EYES made up of hundreds of tiny lenses give excellent all-round vision.

## ID KIT

**TRILOBITE** (TRIL-oh-BYTE)

**MEANING** three lobes

**FOSSILS FOUND** worldwide

**WHEN** Cambrian to Permian

**LENGTH** 0.03 inches to 3 feet

**DIET** carnivores, herbivores, and scavengers

**FOOD** dead organic matter, microorganisms, worms, algae

largest species

These **CLUES** will help you to find where *TRILOBITES* are hiding in this book:

 Some trilobites burrow into the sand. **Look for the sea floor.**

 Many eat worms. **Find their food.**

 Usually found in groups. **Look for more than one trilobite.**

 Now turn to the GLOW-IN-THE-DARK habitat pages to catch a TRILOBITE!

**MANY TRILOBITES** live on the sea floor and wait for things to float by for them to eat. Smaller trilobites burrow into the sediment and munch on dead organic matter.

# JELLYFISH BLOOM CLUES

shallow water     sunlit zone     jellyfish     plankton

**CATCH ME if you can!**

# EURHINOSAURUS
looks like a modern **SWORDFISH**. It is a **FAST** ichthyosaur.

***EURHINOSAURUS'S*** upper jaw is twice as long as its lower jaw, and covered with sidewards-pointing teeth. It is perfect for swiping and stunning fish.

**POWERFUL TAIL** to propel quickly through the water.

**SWORDFISH-LIKE JAWS** to slash and demolish prey.

**POWERFUL, LONG BODY** can leap out of the water to escape predators.

**LARGE FINS** to move quickly through the water.

## ID KIT

**EURHINOSAURUS**

(YOO-rye-NOE-sore-us)

**MEANING** well-nosed lizard

**FOSSILS FOUND** England, Germany

**WHEN** Early Jurassic

**LENGTH** 19 feet

**WEIGHT** 1.5 tons

**DIET** piscivore

**FOOD** fish

These **CLUES** will help you to find where **EURHINOSAURUS** is hiding in this book:

Powerful tail to move quickly and chase down fast-swimming fish. **Find prey.**

Lives far from the shore. **Look for open water.**

Leaps out of the water. **Check above the water surface.**

Now turn to the GLOW-IN-THE-DARK habitat pages to catch **EURHINOSAURUS**!

**A POWERFUL TAIL** and large fins make *Eurhinosaurus* one of the fastest ichthyosaurs. It can chase fish, and escape slow-moving predators.

# LIOPLEURODON
lurches up from the **OCEAN** depths to capture prey at **SPEED**.

**HUGE JAWS** take up one-fifth of *Liopleurodon's* body length. Some of its teeth are 8 inches long and stick out in front to form a vicious trap.

EYES on the top of its head reveal that *Liopleurodon* attacks from below.

HUGE TEETH-FILLED JAWS for grasping prey and tearing through flesh, bone, and muscle.

COLOSSAL RIB MUSCLES for moving its flippers in powerful, fast strokes.

## ID KIT

***LIOPLEURODON***

(LIE-oh-PLOOR-oh-don)

**MEANING** smooth-sided teeth

**FOSSILS FOUND** Europe

**WHEN** Mid to Late Jurassic

**LENGTH** up to 22 feet

**WEIGHT** 1–1.7 tons

**DIET** carnivore

**FOOD** plesiosaurs, ichthyosaurs, marine crocodiles, dolphins

These **CLUES** will help you to find where **LIOPLEURODON** is hiding in this book:

 Eyes on the top of head to attack prey from below. **Look for prey such as dolphins.**

 Preys on ichthyosaurs. **Have you found *Eurhinosaurus* yet?**

 Must surface to breathe. **Check the ocean surface.**

 Now turn to the GLOW-IN-THE-DARK habitat pages to catch *LIOPLEURODON*!

***LIOPLEURODON*** ambushes prey at high speed. Its powerful flippers help it to accelerate quickly to catch ichthyosaurs and other marine animals.

## CORAL REEF CLUES

sand and silt     small stones     fish     worms

# ELASMOSAURUS
uses its extremely **LONG NECK** to sneak up on **SHOALS** of unsuspecting fish.

**INTERLOCKING TEETH** are for trapping, not chewing. *Elasmosaurus* swallows prey whole.

**GOOD EYE-SIGHT** to find small fish, and other small sea creatures such as ammonites and belemnites.

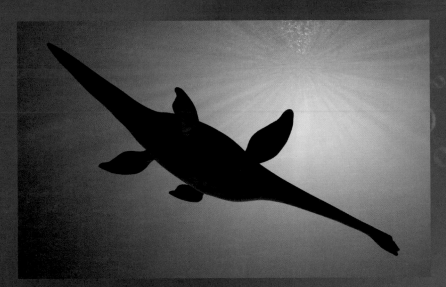

**OCCASIONALLY** *Elasmosaurus* dives to the sea bed to find and swallow rounded pebbles. It might have 150 in its stomach at one time.

**LONG NECK**, up to 23-feet long, which is almost half its body length. Seventy one vertebrae give the neck a snake-like flexibility.

## ID KIT

***ELASMOSAURUS***

(El-LAZZ-mo-SORE-us)

**MEANING** ribbon lizard

**FOSSILS FOUND** USA

**WHEN** Late Cretaceous

**LENGTH** up to 49 feet

**WEIGHT** 2 tons

**DIET** piscivore

**FOOD** fish, ammonites, belemnites

These **CLUES** will help you to find where *ELASMOSAURUS* is hiding in this book:

Catches fish in its interlocking teeth. **Find a shoal of fish.**

Extremely long neck. **Look out for this feature.**

*Elasmosaurus* is the longest plesiosaur ever. **You won't miss it!**

Now turn to the GLOW-IN-THE-DARK habitat pages to catch *ELASMOSAURUS*!

**FOUR PADDLE-SHAPED** flippers to swim through the water.

**ELASMOSAURUS** uses its long neck to reach into a shoal of fish. It is an efficient way to feed. This plesiosaur only has to move its head and neck for a meal rather than wasting energy swimming after fast moving prey.

ELASMOSAURUS can only swim in the direction that its head and neck are pointing in. It is a slow swimmer.

GASTROLITHS, or stones, in the stomach to grind down food. As the stones get worn down, *Elasmosaurus* swallows more.

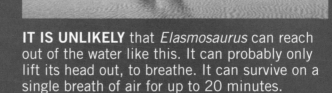

**IT IS UNLIKELY** that *Elasmosaurus* can reach out of the water like this. It can probably only lift its head out, to breathe. It can survive on a single breath of air for up to 20 minutes.

# OPEN SEA CLUES

| open water | fish | dolphins | sunlit surface |

# DUNKLEOSTEUS eats anything in its path. It has a LETHAL set of BLADED jaws.

***EURYPTERUS'S*** tough outer skeleton is no protection from *Dunkleosteus*, whose bite is as powerful as that of a modern alligator.

EACH EYE is shielded by four thick pieces of bone.

ARMOR PLATING of bone up to 2 inches thick.

WIDE MOUTH to capture prey.

RAZOR-SHARP, JAGGED plates instead of teeth. These tear flesh and are part of its jaw bones.

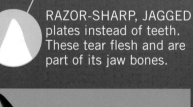

***CLADOSELACHE*** was the first true shark. It was prey to *Dunkleosteus*. The only predator that *Dunkleosteus* had to worry about was a bigger *Dunkleosteus*!

## ID KIT

***DUNKLEOSTEUS***

(DUN-kel-OS-tee-us)

**MEANING** Dunkle's bones

**FOSSILS FOUND** North America, Belgium, Poland, Morocco

**WHEN** Late Devonian

**LENGTH** 33 feet

**WEIGHT** up to 4 tons

**DIET** carnivore

**FOOD** fish, sharks, ammonites

These **CLUES** will help you to find where *DUNKLEOSTEUS* is hiding in this book:

Razor-sharp jaw to tear flesh. **Find its prey.**

Dunkleosteus is a cannibal. **Can you spot other *Dunkleosteus*?**

Huge armored body. **Look out for this feature.**

Now turn to the GLOW-IN-THE-DARK habitat pages to catch *DUNKLEOSTEUS*!

# ORTHACANTHUS
## is similar to XENACANTHUS, but three times BIGGER.

**ORTHACANTHUS** hides amongst dense vegetation to ambush prey. It lives in rivers and swamps alongside the smaller shark, *Xenacanthus.*

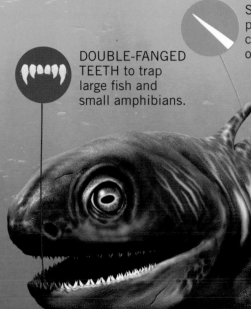

SPIKE to stop other predators from clamping their jaws onto its head.

DOUBLE-FANGED TEETH to trap large fish and small amphibians.

STREAMLINE body to wriggle through densely overgrown swamps and rivers.

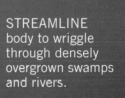

SHORT FINS to prevent it from getting stuck in river debris and vegetation.

## ID KIT

**ORTHACANTHUS**

(ORF-ah-CAN-fus)

**MEANING** vertical spike

**FOSSILS FOUND** Europe, North America

**WHEN** Devonian to Triassic

**LENGTH** up to 10 feet

**DIET** carnivore

**FOOD** fish, amphibians, young *Orthacanthus*

These **CLUES** will help you to find where **ORTHACANTHUS** is hiding in this book:

This shark is a predator.
**Look for its prey.**

Swims in fresh water.
**Find a river.**

Lives alongside *Xenacanthus.*
**Have you found this prehistoric shark?**

Now turn to the GLOW-IN-THE-DARK habitat pages to catch *ORTHACANTHUS!*

**THE GIANT** mammal-like reptile, *Dimetrodon*, lived in swamps in the Late Devonian period. It probably preyed on *Orthacanthus.*

# RIVER CLUES

fresh water    fish    vegetation    amphibians

# SUCHOMIMUS swims through swamps and river deltas looking for FISH and SMALL DINOSAURS.

 LARGE HAND CLAWS to catch fish and slash small dinosaurs.

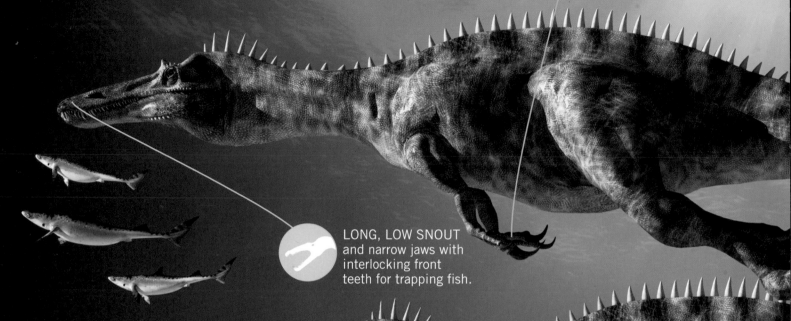

LONG, LOW SNOUT and narrow jaws with interlocking front teeth for trapping fish.

LONG RAZOR-SHARP TEETH for eating fish and small dinosaurs.

## ID KIT

*SUCHOMIMUS* (SOOK-o-MIME-us)

**MEANING** crocodile mimic

**FOSSILS FOUND** Niger

**WHEN** Early Cretaceous

**LENGTH** 35 feet

**HEIGHT** 12 feet at hips

**WEIGHT** 5-6 tons

**DIET** carnivore

**FOOD** fish, dinosaurs, pterosaurs, crocodiles, carrion (dead animals)

These CLUES will help you to find where *SUCHOMIMUS* is hiding in this book:

 Huge thumb claw for stabbing fish. **Find *Suchomimus's* favorite food.**

 Hunts small dinosaurs and crocodiles. **Look for prey.**

 Roams river deltas, lagoons, and swamps. **Seek out fresh water.**

 Now turn to the GLOW-IN-THE-DARK habitat pages to catch *SUCHOMIMUS.*

 HUGE THUMB CLAW to stab fish. It is 7.5 inches long!

**ON LAND,** small dinosaurs are on the menu. *Suchomimus* grips prey in its mouth while slashing at its neck with its claws.

**SUCHOMIMUS** roams river deltas and lagoons looking for food. It uses its huge thumb claw and needle-like teeth to seize slippery fish. But it is also an opportunist. *Suchomimus* will scavenge dead animals and eat pterosaurs and small dinosaurs, too.

 PADDLE-SHAPED FEET for moving through the water easily.

 LONG TAIL to help balance on land.

DENSE BONES to help with buoyancy in the water.

**THIS DINOSAUR** hunts in the water and on the land like a modern-day crocodile. The nostrils on the top of its nose enable it to breathe when partly submerged in the water. *Suchomimus's* flat, paddle-shaped feet push it swiftly along in the water.

41

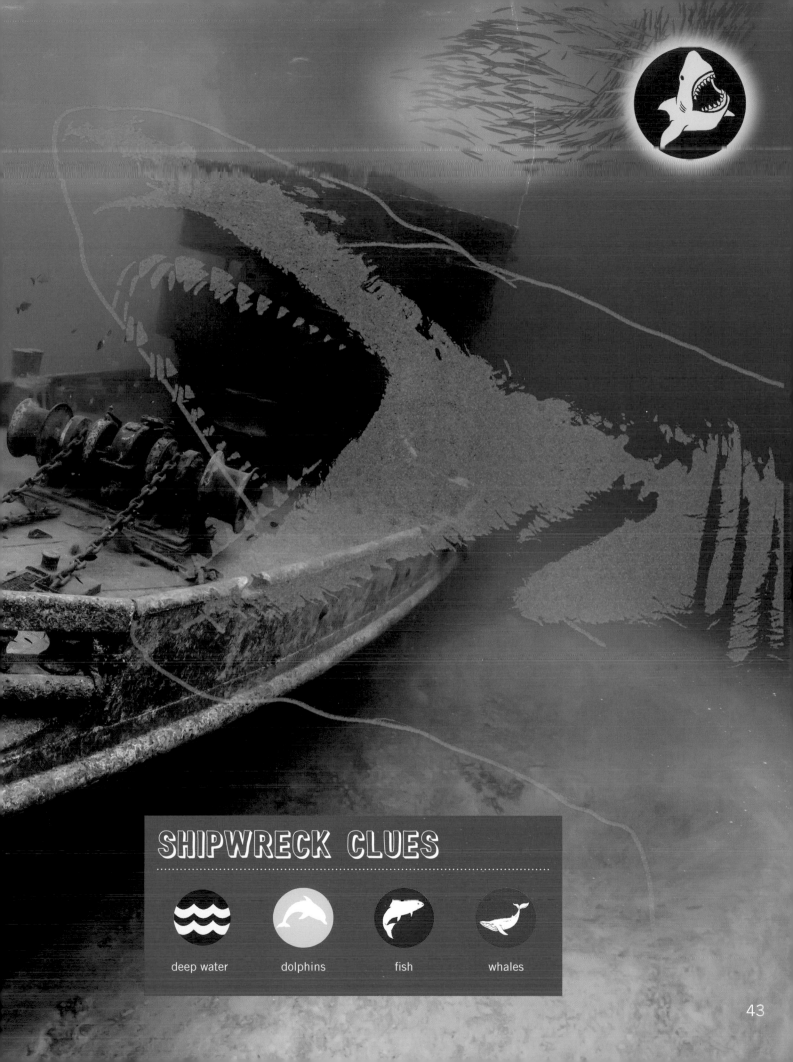

# SHIPWRECK CLUES

deep water     dolphins     fish     whales

# EURYPTERUS
uses its sharp **CLAWS** and vicious spines to **SHRED** prey.

**TAIL CURVES up** and over like a modern scorpion. It does not have the ability to sting.

**TOUGH OUTER SKELETON**, which *Eurypterus* sheds in order to grow bigger.

**FOUR HUNDRED MILLION** years ago, in shallow Silurian seas, *Eurypterus* was the top predator. In deeper waters it would be an easy meal for 30-foot-long *Giant Orthocone*.

**PADDLE-LIKE LEGS** to swim and steer through the water.

## ID KIT

*EURYPTERUS* (YOU-rip-TEH-rus)

**MEANING** wide wing

**COMMON NAME** sea scorpion

**FOSSILS FOUND** USA, Canada, Europe

**WHEN** Silurian

**LENGTH** 3 inches to 4.5 feet

**DIET** carnivore

**FOOD** small animals on the seabed, such as worms, crustaceans, and fish

largest species

These **CLUES** will help you to find where *EURYPTERUS* is hiding in this book:

 Often found in groups. **Find other *Eurypterus*.**

 Safe in shallow waters. **Find a sunlit ocean.**

 Long spines to sense prey in the sand. **Look for worms on the ocean floor.**

 Now turn to the GLOW-IN-THE-DARK habitat pages to catch *EURYPTERUS*!

GILLS TO ABSORB oxygen from the water and from the air. *Eurypterus* is adapted to live in water and on land.

**DURING A FULL MOON** swarms of *Eurypterus* head to the coast to mate and to molt. Just like modern crabs, they crawl out of their old shells to reveal a softer shell beneath. There are less predators in shallow waters, so the *Eurypterus* stay there until their new shells harden.

FRONT PINCERS to tear prey into pieces small enough to fit into its mouth.

FORWARD-FACING compound eyes to judge exactly when its pincers are in striking range of prey.

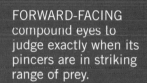

LONG SPINES on the front limbs are sensitive to vibrations in sand and silt.

**EURYPTERUS** has long spines that can detect worms, fish, and small shrimp-like creatures to eat.

# DID YOU CATCH THEM?

Did you find the glow-in-the-dark sharks and prehistoric sea and river monsters?
Check the pictures below to make sure that you found them all.

*Shonisaurus*, *Dunkleosteus*, and *Dakosaurus* swim into the big school of barracuda. They all eat sea fish. *Dunkleosteus* might also try to eat *Dakosaurus*.

*Deinosuchus* waits patiently at the bottom to snap up turtles. *Suchomimus* catches fish with its razor-sharp thumb claws.

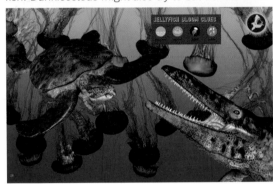

*Archelon* finds plenty of food amongst the jellyfish in the sunlit zone of the ocean. *Tylosaurus* is after *Archelon*. It makes a surprise attack from below.

*Styxosaurus* reaches into a shoal of fish on the coral reef. Trilobites and *Eurypterus* hunt for worms and crustaceans in the shallow waters.

*Eurhinosaurus* hunts for fish in the open sea. *Liopleurodon* hunts *Eurhinosaurus*. The large ichthyosaur leaps out of the water and escapes.

*Orthacanthus* slithers through the vegetation looking for large fish and amphibians. *Xenacanthus* is nearby hunting smaller freshwater fish.

*Livyatan* prowls the shipwreck looking for whales, sharks, or dolphins. But *Megalodon* is in its territory. The two mighty sea monsters battle it out.

*Elasmosaurus* sneaks up on a shoal of fish in the kelp forest. *Kronosaurus* lunges forward to clamp onto *Elasmosaurus's* extraordinarily long neck.